But everything changed
From joy to despair
When Hippo discovered
That Bird wasn't there.

He noticed Bird missing
At the first break of dawn
After rubbing his eyes
With a stretch and a yawn.

'But how could she leave
Without saying goodbye?'
He searched for a reason
But he didn't know why.

Perhaps she decided
That today was the day
She'd return to her tree
And just flew away.

But Hippo knew something
That troubled him more
If he wanted to find her
He'd have to explore.

So off Hippo went
To places unknown
In search of his friend
Afraid and alone.

He waded through swamps
That went on for miles
With deadly piranhas
And huge crocodiles.

He was followed by wolves
As they prowled in their pack
Through the shadowy forest
All set to attack.

The wolves drew in closer
As he quickened his stride
'Til he came to a bridge
With nowhere to hide.

The bridge wobbled gently
As it swayed in the breeze
And as Hippo stepped on
He went weak at the knees.

He felt the bridge crack
Right under his toes
And as he looked down
Poor Hippo just froze.

CRASH!

The bridge broke apart
With an almighty CRASH!

SPLASH!

And he dropped to the river
With a thundering SPLASH!

The river rushed by
As it dragged him along
And he tried to swim out
But the flow was too strong.

And as he got closer
To the edge of the cliff
He was not just afraid
But completely scared stiff!

He plunged to the bottom
All flustered and shaken
As he wondered how far
The river would take him.

He was carried ashore
After drifting for hours
To a tree on an island
Surrounded by flowers.

He thought about Bird
And how happy she'd be
To find such a place
With this wonderful tree.

Although it seemed perfect
He was there all alone
And he had no idea
How to find his way home.

The day had been long
Since leaving that morning
And he felt so worn out
He couldn't help yawning.

And just as he did
Came the biggest surprise
As Bird just flew out
Of his mouth, open wide!

She must have flown in
At the first break of dawn
As Hippo woke up
With a stretch and a yawn.

He just didn't notice
Being still half asleep
That Bird was indeed
Just cleaning his teeth.

He couldn't believe
That there, all the while
Bird had been with him
Which made Hippo smile.

What a wonderful feeling
So strange but so nice
To have found his best friend
In this lost paradise.

THE END